THE MUSIC OF
PAUL McCARTNEY
1973 - 2001

WISE PUBLICATIONS

part of The Music Sales Group

LONDON · NEW YORK · PARIS · SYDNEY · COPENHAGEN · BERLIN · MADRID · TOKYO

Published by:
Wise Publications,
8/9 Frith Street, London W1D 3JB, England.

Exclusive Distributors:
Music Sales Limited,
Distribution Centre, Newmarket Road, Bury St Edmunds,
Suffolk IP33 3YB, England.
Music Sales Pty Limited,
120 Rothschild Avenue, Rosebery, NSW 2018, Australia.

Order No. AM979000
ISBN 1-84449-200-1
This book © Copyright 2003 by Wise Publications.
All photographs © Copyright 2003 MPL Communications Ltd.

Cover design by Roger Huggett/Sinc.
Music arranged by Roger Day and Jack Long.
Music engraved by Paul Ewers Music Design.
Printed and bound in Malta.

Your Guarantee of Quality
As publishers, we strive to produce every book to the highest commercial standards.
The music has been freshly engraved and the book has been carefully designed to
minimise awkward page turns and to make playing from it a real pleasure.
Particular care has been given to specifying acid-free, neutral-sized paper made from
pulps which have not been elemental chlorine bleached. This pulp is from farmed
sustainable forests and was produced with special regard for the environment.
Throughout, the printing and binding have been planned to ensure a sturdy,
attractive publication which should give years of enjoyment.
If your copy fails to meet our high standards, please inform us and we will
gladly replace it.

www.musicsales.com
www.mplcommunications.com

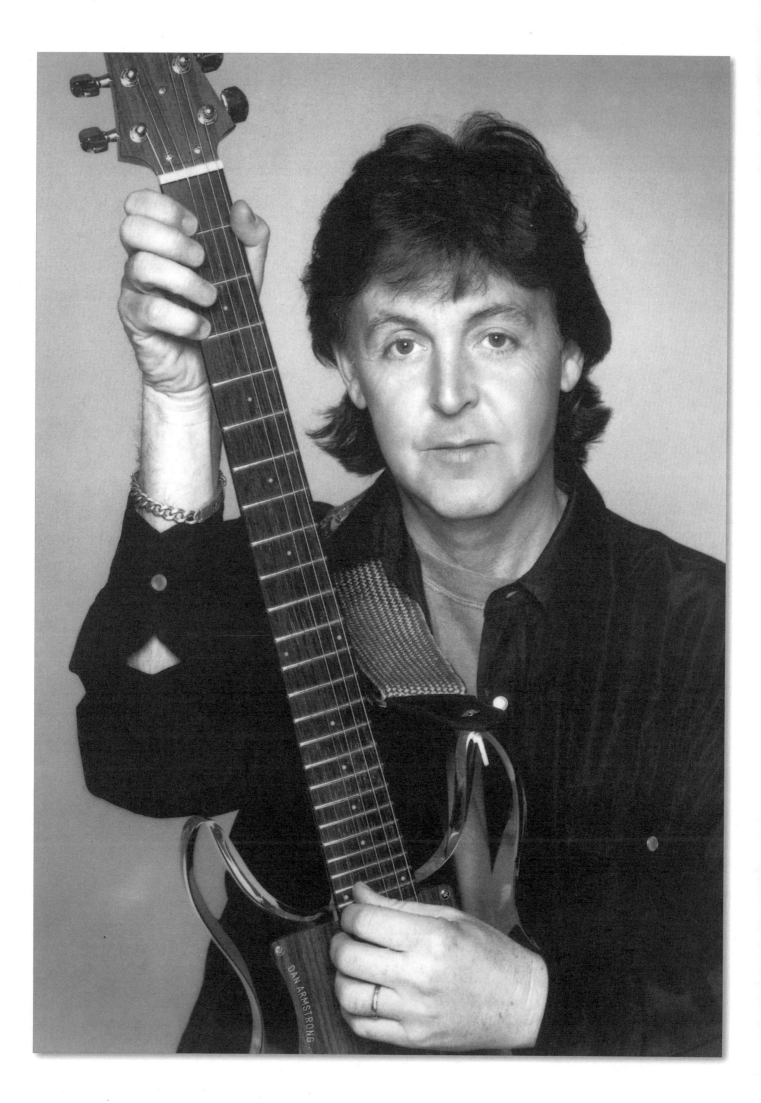

AFTER THE BALL / MILLION MILES

Words & Music by Paul McCartney

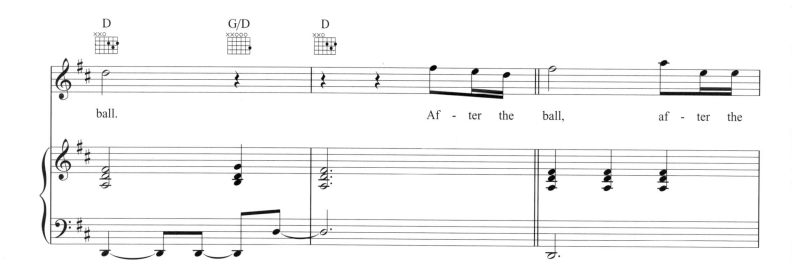

14

16

BEWARE MY LOVE

Words & Music by Paul McCartney & Linda McCartney

17

no, no, no.____

must be wrong,____ ba - by. Yeah.__ 1, 3. But I don't be - lieve____
2. *Instrumental*

that he's the one,____

but if you in - sist,____ I must be wrong.____

BAND ON THE RUN

Words & Music by Paul McCartney & Linda McCartney

24

BEAUTIFUL NIGHT

Words & Music by Paul McCartney

Some-one's gone out fish-ing, — some-one's high and dry.

Some-one's on a mis-sion to the lone-ly Lo-re-lei.

Some folks got a vi-sion of a cas-tle in the

sky.   And I'm left strand - ed

won - d'ring why. ———

You and me to - ge - ther, ——— no - thing feels so good, —
2. *(see block lyric)*

e - ven if I get a med - al from my lo - cal neigh - bour - hood.

32

Verse 2:
Some boat's on the ocean,
We're here in this room,
Seems to me the perfect way to spend an afternoon.
We can look for castles, pretty castles in the sky.
No more wondering, wondering why.

BLUEBIRD

Words & Music by Paul McCartney & Linda McCartney

34

CALL ME BACK AGAIN

Words & Music by Paul McCartney & Linda McCartney

Fairly Slow (In Four)

VERSE

Well, when I, when I was just a lit-tle baby boy, Ev-'ry night

call _____ me back _ a - gain.   Well, when   gain.   Come on and

call _____ me back _ a - gain.   Come on and

38

call _____ me back _ a - gain.   Come on and

Additional Lyric:
Verse:
    Well when I, when I was just a little baby boy,
    Every night, every night I would call
    Because your number brought me joy.
    Oh, I've called your name every night since then,
Chorus:
    But I ain't never no no no no never heard you calling me.
    Come on and call me back again.
    Come on and call me back again.

C'MON PEOPLE

Words & Music by Paul McCartney

39

Oh__ yeah,   oh   yeah.__

C'-mon   peo - ple, let the   world be - gin;__   we've got a fu - ture and it's

just_____   rush - ing in.__

Ad lib. Vocal

43

COMING UP

Words & Music by Paul McCartney

Moderately

VERSES

(1) You want a love   to last for ev - er
(2) You want a friend   you can re - ly on
(3) You want some peace   and un - der-stand - ing

one that will ne - ver   fade a - way.__   I want to help you
one who will ne - ver   fade a - way.__   And if you're search-ing__ for__
so ev - 'ry-bo - dy   can__ be free.   I know that we can__ get__

44

45

EBONY AND IVORY

Words & Music by Paul McCartney

49

 iv - or - y __ live to - ge-ther in per - fect har - mo - ny, __ side by

side on my pian - o key - board, oh _ Lord, why _ don't we? _

51

53

GOLDEN EARTH GIRL

Words & Music by Paul McCartney

1. Gold - en earth girl,
2. Good clear wa - ter
3. Na - ture's lov - er

57

THE MUSIC OF
PAUL McCARTNEY
1973 - 2001

HOPE OF DELIVERANCE

Words & Music by Paul McCartney

58

1. I will al - ways be   hop - ing,   hop - ing,
(2.) - stand   some - day,   one day.
(3.) mind   know - ing,   know - ing

you will al - ways be   hold - ing,
You will un - der - stand,   al - ways,
that you would - n't mind   go - ing,

I'M CARRYING

Words & Music by Paul McCartney

64

JET

Words & Music by Paul McCartney & Linda McCartney

Jet!

Jet!

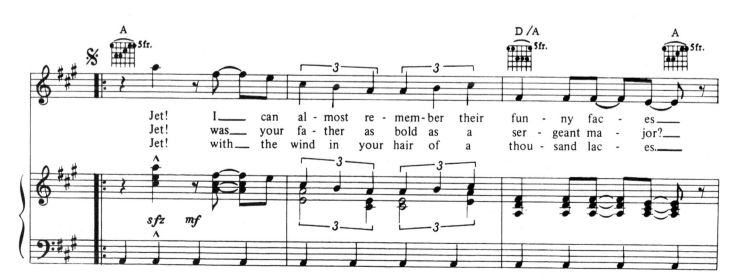

Jet! I__ can al - most re - mem-ber their fun - ny fac - es__

Jet! was__ your fa - ther as bold as a ser - geant ma - jor?__

Jet! with__ the wind in your hair of a thou - sand lac - es.__

68

la - dy____ suf - fra - gette.____ Jet! Oo_____

Jet! Oo_____

FROM A LOVER TO A FRIEND

Words & Music by Paul McCartney

LET 'EM IN

Words & Music by Paul McCartney & Linda McCartney

75

Do me a fa - vor, o - pen the door___ and let 'em in.___

LET ME ROLL IT

Words & Music by Paul McCartney & Linda McCartney

78

THE MUSIC OF
PAUL McCARTNEY
1973 - 2001

LISTEN TO WHAT THE MAN SAID

Words & Music by Paul McCartney & Linda McCartney

THE MUSIC OF
PAUL McCARTNEY
1973 - 2001

LITTLE WILLOW

Words & Music by Paul McCartney

84

85

now ___ and for-ev-er al-ways came too soon. ___

Ah ___

Ah ___

Ah ___

Ah ___

Ah ___

Ah ___

Ah ___

lit-tle wil-low. ___

87

THE MUSIC OF
PAUL McCARTNEY
1973 - 2001

LOVE IN SONG

Words & Music by Paul McCartney & Linda McCartney

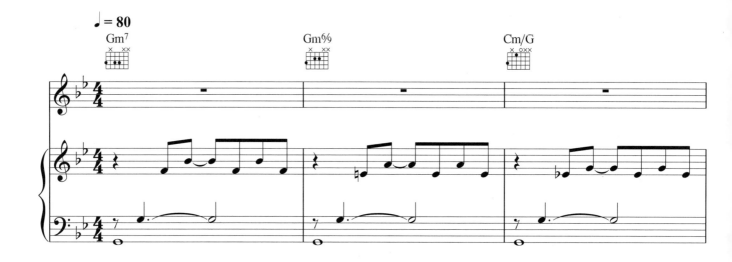

88

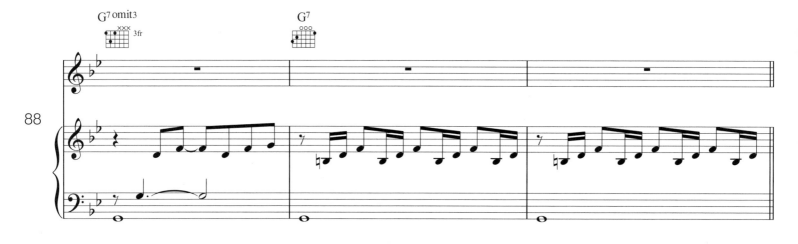

1. My heart___ cries out___ for love___ and all___ that goes___ with lov-
2. My, you're so fine___ when love___ is mine,___ I can't___ go wrong,
3. My eye___ cries out___ a tear, still born, mis-un-der-stand-

LOVELIEST THING

Words & Music by Paul McCartney

91

92

94

MAMUNIA

Words & Music by Paul McCartney & Linda McCartney

It might have been a bright blue day, but rain clouds had to come this way. They're
seed is wait - ing in the earth for rain to come and give him birth. It's

wat - 'ring ev - er - y - thing that they can see.
all he real - ly needs to set him free.

A

So the

MRS. VANDEBILT

Words & Music by Paul McCartney & Linda McCartney

105

Down in the jun-gle, liv-ing in a tent, you don't use mon-ey and you don't pay rent; you don't ev-en know the time, but you don't mind.

MULL OF KINTYRE

Words & Music by Paul McCartney & Denny Laine

112

moun-tains__ with val-leys__ of green. Past paint-ed des-erts__ the

sun-set's on fire__ as he car-ries me home__ to the Mull__ of Kin-

tyre. Mull__ of Kin-tyre Oh mist roll-ing in from__ the

sea, my de-sire is al-ways to be here Oh Mull__ of Kin-

tyre.

Sweep through____ the heath-er____ like deer in the glen Car-ry me back to the days I knew then. Nights when we

115

NINETEEN HUNDRED AND EIGHTY FIVE

Words & Music by Paul McCartney

116

1, 3. No one ev - er left a - live_ in nine - teen hund - red and eight - y five_ will ev -
2. My ma - ma said a time_ would come when I would find my - self in_ love_

- er_ do.
_____ with_ you.
She may be right,_ she may be fine;_ she
I did - n't think,_ I nev - er dreamed that

may get love_ but she won't get mine 'cause I_____ got_ you. }
I would be_ a - round_ to see it all_____ come true. }
Woh_____ I,_

117

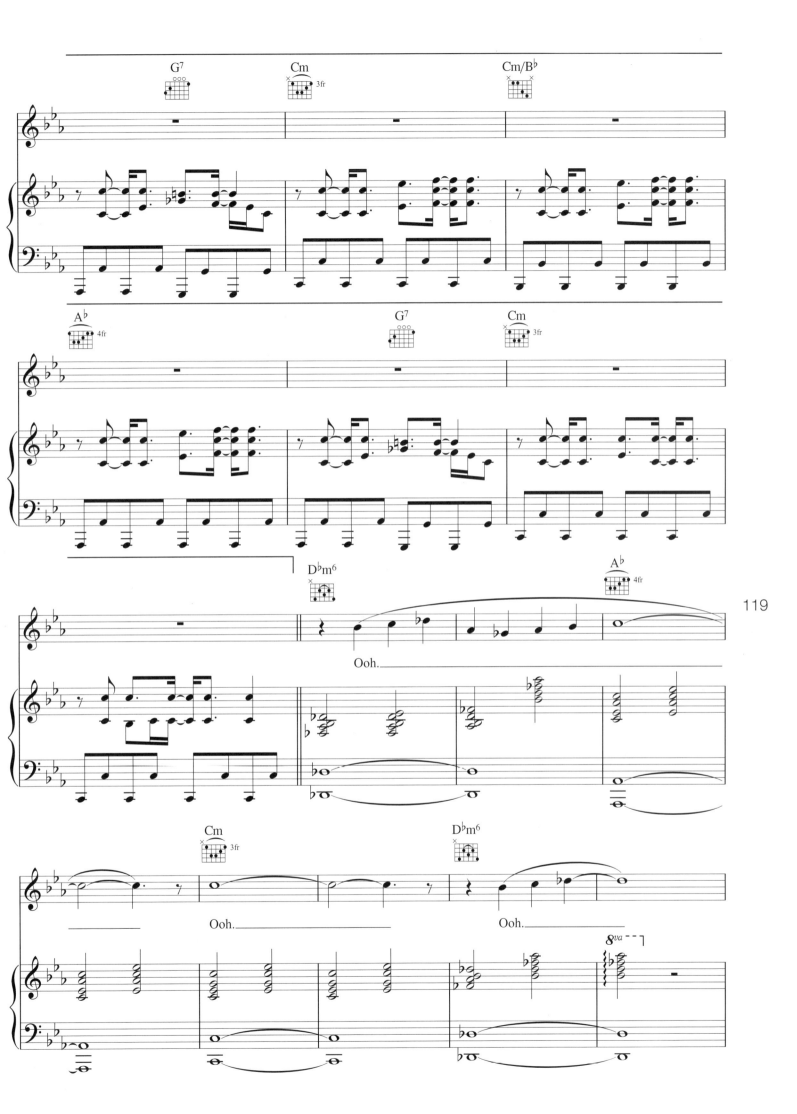

NO MORE LONELY NIGHTS

Words & Music by Paul McCartney

121

122

ONCE UPON A LONG AGO

Words & Music by Paul McCartney

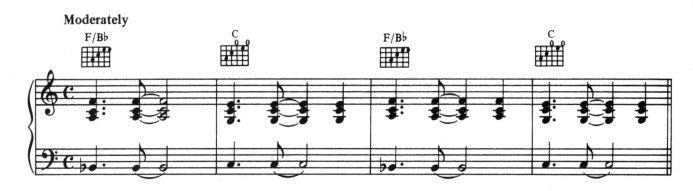

Moderately

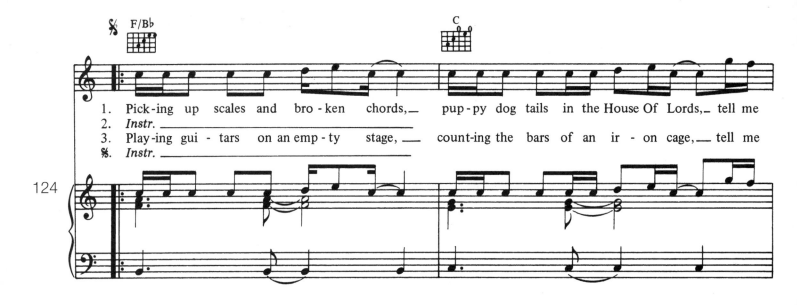

1. Pick-ing up scales and bro-ken chords,— pup-py dog tails in the House Of Lords,— tell me
2. *Instr.* _____
3. Play-ing gui-tars on an emp-ty stage, ___ count-ing the bars of an ir-on cage,— tell me
𝄋. *Instr.* _____

124

dar - ling, what can it mean?____
dar - ling, what can it mean?____

(1.) Mak-ing up moons in a min-or key, ___ what have those tunes got to do with me, ___ tell me
(2.) Blow-ing bal-loons on a win-dy day, ___ des-o-late dunes with a lot to say, ___ tell me
(3.) Pick-ing up scales and bro-ken chords, ___ pup-py dog tails in the House Of Lords, ___ tell me

1,2.

dar - ling, where have you been? ___
dar - ling, what have you seen? ___
dar - ling, what does it mean? ___

(1,2.) Once up-on ___ a long a-go, child-ren searched ___ for
%. Instr. (cont'd)

127

ONE OF THESE DAYS

Words & Music by Paul McCartney

all we ev-er want-ed to be.

D.C. al Coda
To Coda ⊕

⊕ *Coda*

4. One of these days,___ when my feet are on the ground,

I'm gon-na look___ a-round___ and see;___

see what's right,___

131

THE MUSIC OF
PAUL McCARTNEY
1973 - 2001

THE OTHER ME

Words & Music by Paul McCartney

♩ = 100

132

1. I know I was a cra-zy fool_ for treat-ing you the way I did;
(2.) know it does-n't take a lot_ to have a lit-tle self con-trol;
(3.) wish that I could take it back,_ I'd like to make a diff-'rent mood;_

_ but some-thing took a hold of me_ and act-
_ but ev-'ry time that I for-got,_ well I land-
_ and if you let me try a-gain_ I'll have_

- ed like a dust-bin lid._ I did-n't give a se-cond thought_ to
- ed in an-oth-er hole._ But ev-'ry time you pull me out_ I
_ a bet-ter at-ti-tude._ But I know that one and one makes two,_ and

PIPES OF PEACE

Words & Music by Paul McCartney

136

All round the world
What do you say
(what do you say? _____)

lit-tle chil-dren be-ing born to the world,
will the hu-man race be run in a day,
(in a day _____)

got to give them all we
or will someone save this

can till the war is won: __
plan-et we're play-ing on? __

then will the work be done. __
Is it the on-ly one? __

(What are we going to do?)

Help them to learn __ (help them to learn __) songs of joy in-stead of burn, ba-by burn __ (burn, ba-by burn __
Help me to learn _____ songs of joy in-stead of burn, ba-by burn __
Help them to see __ (help them to see __) that the people here are like you and me __ (like you and me __

137

let us show them how to play   the pipes of peace,
won't you show me how to play (how to play_) the pipes of peace (pipes of peace_)
let us show them how to play (how to play_) the pipes of peace (pipes of peace_)

play   the pipes of peace. _____

Ooh _____

PUT IT THERE

Words & Music by Paul McCartney

that's what a fa - ther said ____ to his young ___ son.

I don't care ____ if it weighs a ton, ___

___ as long as you and I are here, put it there. ___

___ Long as you and I are

OLD SIAM, SIR

Words & Music by Paul McCartney

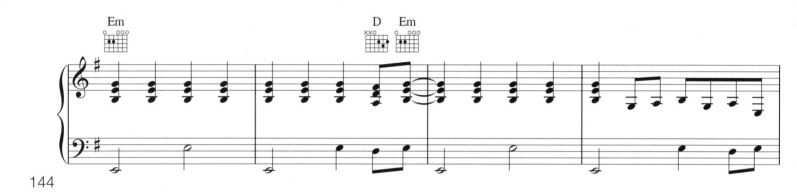

144

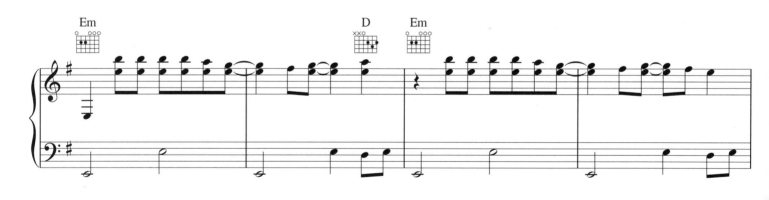

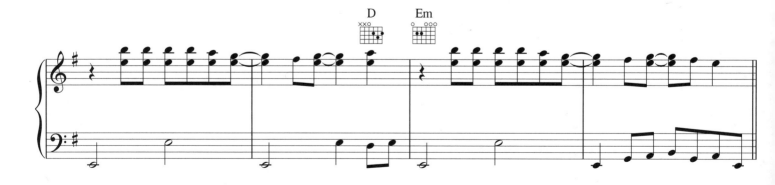

SAY SAY SAY

Words & Music by Paul McCartney & Michael Jackson

1. Say, say, say, what you want, but don't play games
2. Go, go, go where you want, but don't leave me
3. You, you, you can nev-er say that I'm not the one

149

look at my face: these tears ain't dry - ing.

D.S. al Coda

Coda

Ad lib. Vocal

153

Repeat ad lib. to fade

SILLY LOVE SONGS

Words & Music by Paul McCartney & Linda McCartney

154

157

158

It is-n't sil-ly, no, it is-n't sil-ly,

Love is-n't sil-ly at all.

How___ can I tell___ you a-bout___ my___ loved one?

How___ can I tell___ you a-bout___ my___ loved one?

I love you.

159

161

songs.

But I look a - round me and I see_____ it is - n't so. Oh, no.____

Some peo - ple wan - na fill the world_____ with sil - ly love songs,____

And what's wrong with that?_____

SOUVENIR

Words & Music by Paul McCartney

163

164

166

Verse 2:
When you're crying like a poor little child
And you're feeling like you never could be reconciled
Don't forget a word of what I'm saying

Verse 3:
Everybody's got a handful of fear,
But tomorrow it may only be a souvenir
Of the way it was till it went away.

If you want me to tell me now,
If I can be of any help tell me how.
Let me love you like a friend,
Every little thing is gonna come right in the end.

THE MUSIC OF
PAUL McCARTNEY
1973 - 2001

SO BAD

Words & Music by Paul McCartney

There is a pain____ in-side my heart;____ you mean so much____ ____ to me.____ Girl, I love you; girl, I love you so bad.____

171

SUMMER'S DAY SONG

Words & Music by Paul McCartney

172

world will soon be wak - ing to a sum - mer's day.

Some - one's sleep - ing   through a bad dream;_____   to - mor - row_____

TAKE IT AWAY

Words & Music by Paul McCartney

176

Take it a-way____ want to hear you play____ till the lights____ go down.

(2.) (Down down___) Take it a-way____ don't you want____ to stay____

____ till there's no____ one else____ a-round.

178

THIS ONE

Words & Music by Paul McCartney

181

feel - ing like the tim - ing was - n't quite right? ___

What kind of ma - gic might have worked if we had stayed calm,

184

could - n't I have giv - en you ___ a bet - ter life? ___

Did you ev - er take me in your

185

TUG OF WAR

Words & Music by Paul McCartney

186

189

In a time to come __ we will be danc-ing to the beat played on a diff - 'rent

D.S. al Coda
a tempo

drum. We will be danc-ing to the beat played on a diff -'rent drum.
It's a tug of war.

ritard.

190

CODA

rall.

WANDERLUST

Words & Music by Paul McCartney

1. Light   out   wan - der - lust,
2. Take   us   from   the   dark,

191

195

THE MUSIC OF
PAUL McCARTNEY
1973 - 2001

WARM AND BEAUTIFUL

Words & Music by Paul McCartney & Linda McCartney

196

never fades a - way. Love, faith and

hope are beau - ti - ful, when your world is touched by sad - ness,

to each his own is won - der - ful, love will nev - er die.

Sun - light's morn - ing glo - ry tells the sto - ry of our love.

197

WATERFALLS

Words & Music by Paul McCartney

Don't go jump-ing wa-ter-falls please keep to the
2nd time instr.
Don't go chas-ing po-lar bears in the great un -
Don't run af-ter mo-tor cars please stay on the

lake peo-ple who jump wa-ter-falls some-times can make
known some big friend-ly po-lar bear might want to take
side, some-one's gloss-y mo-tor car might take you for

199

_ mis-takes _
_ you home _
_ a ride, _

and I need love _ yeah

WINTER ROSE/LOVE AWAKE

Words & Music by Paul McCartney

1. All through the sum-mer I have fol-lowed you a-round,____
Verse 2 instrumental

204

207

WITH A LITTLE LUCK

Words & Music by Paul McCartney

Medium tempo

With a lit-tle luck,__ we can help it out.__ We can make this whole__
and a lit-tle luck,__ we can clear it up.__ We can bring it in __
With a lit-tle push,__ we could set it off.__ We can send it rock-

lit-tle luck.__ With a lit-tle luck, a lit-tle luck, a lit-tle luck.__ With a

lit-tle luck.__ With a lit-tle luck.__ With a lit-tle luck, a lit-tle luck, a...

WINEDARK OPEN SEA

Words & Music by Paul McCartney

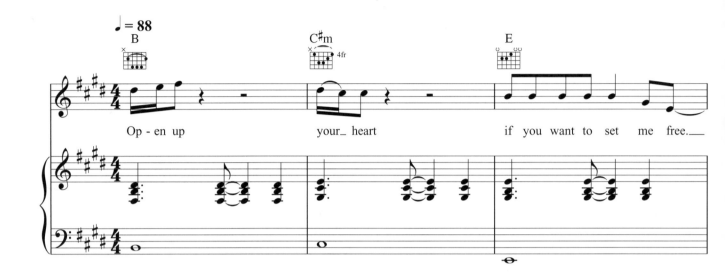

Op - en up your heart if you want to set me free.

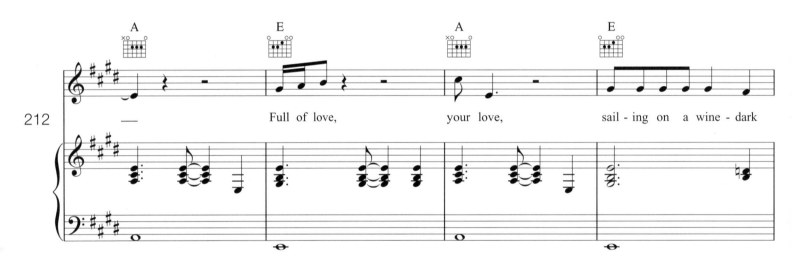

Full of love, your love, sail - ing on a wine - dark

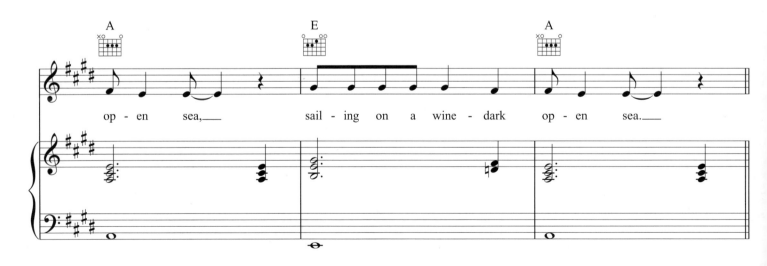

op - en sea, sail - ing on a wine - dark op - en sea.

Sail - ing on a wine - dark op - en sea.___ Sail - ing on a wine - dark op - en sea.___

a tempo

1-3.

4.

I feel love for you now,___ I feel love___ for you right now.___

216

YOU GAVE ME THE ANSWER

Words & Music by Paul McCartney & Linda McCartney

217

218

YOUR LOVING FLAME

Words & Music by Paul McCartney

222